This book belongs to

_____

You Don't Need a Cape to Be a Hero

HERO!!

by Dr. Sherryl Carter, Ed.D.

RoseDog 🐾 Books
PITTSBURGH, PENNSYLVANIA 15238

RoseDog Books
585 Alpha Drive, Suite 103
Pittsburgh, PA 15238
Visit our website at *www.rosedogbookstore.com*

ISBN: 978-1-63867-841-0
eISBN: 978-1-63867-786-4

Dedication:

This book is dedicated to the memory of my Father Mr. Robert Lloyd Carter, Sr. who will forever be my hero. It is also dedicated to my mother and son and to my family and loved ones who constantly "run to my rescue" as we face the challenges of life together.

"I don't want to be a hero
I want to run and jump
and have a lot of fun."

"Mommy says think of the disease as the villain and the mask helps you fight and protects you while you run."

"The mask helps you defend yourself and others whenever you go outside. The covid-19 villain will see that you wear the mask and will run away and hide".

"Wash your hands while you count to twenty then add another ten. Also use hand sanitizer it will be your best friend."

"If you cough or sneeze use your elbow or your sleeve. Keep your germs to yourself and we'll win the battle with this enemy disease."

"Wear your mask no matter what you do, you will save yourself and others from a very scary fate and you will be a hero who doesn't wear a cape."

About the author

Dr. Sherryl Carter, is a graduate of the University of Southern California has been a professional educator for 20 years serving as a School Superintendent, Administrator, Teacher and Counselor in local California Public Schools.

The End

CPSIA information can be obtained
at www.ICGtesting.com
Printed in the USA
BVHW051125021121
620551BV00007B/867